که هستیم؟
Who Are We?

(دری - انگلیسی)
(Dari – English)

by Anneke Forzani
illustrated by Maria Russo
translated by Mujeeb Shinwari

Language Lizard
Basking Ridge

Visit www.LanguageLizard.com/Harmony for additional teaching resources, activities, and English audio for this book.

Who Are We? Dari - English
Text copyright © 2021 Anneke Forzani
Illustration copyright © 2021 Maria Russo
Published by Language Lizard
Basking Ridge, NJ 07920
info@LanguageLizard.com

Visit us at www.LanguageLizard.com

First edition 2021

Library of Congress Control Number: 2021919710

ISBN: 978-1-63685-105-1 (Print)

ما که هستیم؟
Who are we?

ما چهره های زیادی هستیم.

We are many faces.

ما اعتقادات زیادی داریم.

We are many faiths.

ما فرهنگ های زیادی هستیم.

We are many cultures.

ما خانواده های
زیادی هستیم.

**We are many
families.**

ما به زبانهای زیادی صحبت می کنیم.

We speak many languages.

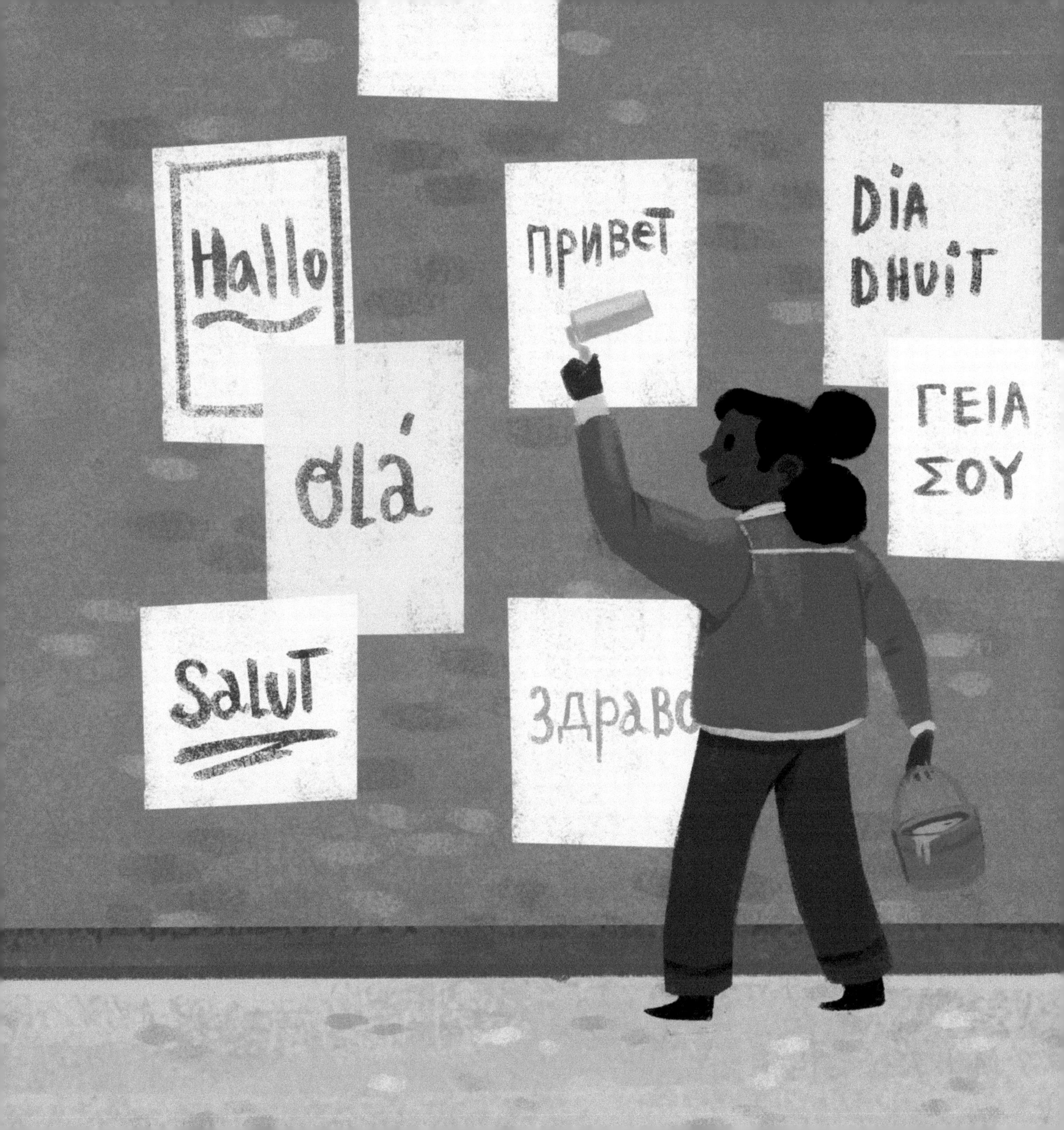
Hallo
привет
Dia
Dhuit
Olá
Γεια
Σου
Salut
здраво

ما چیزها را متفاوت می بینیم.

We see things differently.

ما به کمک به
دیگران اعتقاد داریم.

We believe in helping others.

ما به تغییر اعتقاد داریم.
We believe in change.

ما به بخشش
اعتقاد داریم.

**We believe in
forgiveness.**

وقتی دور هم جمع می شویم ،

When we come together,

ما یک شاهکار هستیم.

we are a masterpiece.